Sofia
and the
spectacular
Outfit

BONNEY
PRESS

Published by Bonney Press,
an imprint of Hinkler Books Pty Ltd 2019
45–55 Fairchild Street
Heatherton Victoria 3202 Australia
www.hinkler.com

BONNEY
PRESS

Story by Katie Hewat
Biographies by Debra Thomas
Illustrations by Eugene Smolenceva

Editorial: Emily Murray
Design: Bianca Zuccolo
Publishing Manager: Jennifer Bilos

ISBN: 978 1 4889 1451 5

Printed and bound in China

Sofia
and the
spectacular
Outfit

Katie Hewat

Eugene Smolenceva

I love clothing and shoes and all kinds of fashion.
I'm original, creative – style is my passion.

I express how I feel in the way that I dress.
I'm always myself; nothing more, nothing less!

I dress how I feel, from my head to my feet –
be it punk or glam rock or just super-sweet.

When happy, I choose clothes that are bright and gay;

when gloomy, they're yellow to wash sadness away.

When nervous, I'll wear something fun or all frilly to remind me life's good and to worry is silly!

When I'm excited, I shimmer and shine

with a glittery outfit that can only be mine!

This week, there's a fun dress-up day at my school.
I'm determined to wear something different and cool.

There's going to be a show and a prize
for the very best outfit, costume or disguise!

Mum has some old boxes up in the attic,
and what's in them has made me excited, ecstatic!

There are dresses and hats and even some shoes;
I know there'll be something in here I can use.

At the bottom I find some old denim flares
and a flowery headband that a hippy girl wears.

I imagine myself as a seventies queen;
I'm peaceful and happy and feeling serene.

I'm totally thrilled as I pull out a pair
of black leather boots that I can't wait to wear.

I pair the boots up with a funky red frock
and feel like I'm ready to dance to some rock!

I uncover a cool diamante-clad hat,
which I put on and look around this way and that.

I add a cute skirt that fans out as I twirl,
and with some old boots I'm a rodeo girl!

These clothes are so great that I'm finding it hard
to pick which to wear and which to discard.

Then in my mind sparks an awesome idea,
and soon it ignites – becomes totally clear!

I pair bright, coloured tights with a light, flowy dress,
Then a long hippy coat, which I know is excess!

I add a hat and some boots and now I can see
that the look I've created is totally me.

When I turn up at school on our dressing-up day,
I see such cool outfits that I'm blown away.

Witches and mermaids and pirates and elves,
and outfits like mine that kids made all themselves.

We all share the spotlight, walking out in a row:
personalities, creations and talents on show.

When it's my turn I walk with a confident stride –

the crowd gives a cheer and I'm bursting with pride!

At the end I'm so happy, I can't help but smile:
I've been given the award for 'most spectacular style'.

I knew it would happen; I knew I could do it!
I'll never give up once I set my mind to it.

The Women Who Inspired Sofia

As Sofia knows, style is fun! To be confident in who you are, express your personality and share your story through your clothing is what makes fashion so exciting. Sofia was not afraid to be her creative and bold self with her choices – and she was recognised as having the 'most spectacular style'! There are many amazingly successful women in fashion. These women have not only followed their own dreams but have also unlocked this world for other women by encouraging them to be themselves and share their originality with the world. Some of these amazing women and their stories are below.

Coco Chanel

'A girl should be two things:
who and what she wants.'

19 AUGUST 1883 – 10 JANUARY 1971
FRANCE

Coco's success in fashion is akin to a Cinderella story – if Cinderella grew up to be the fairy godmother that made beautiful dresses. Coco was born into a poor household. After her mother died, she was sent to an orphanage run by nuns. It was the knowledge of textiles that she gained here that made her one of the most successful designers in the world, as she later used them in the clothes she made for her wealthy clients. Coco's style is one of the most distinctive in fashion, teaming oversized costume jewellery with clothes that are comfortable for women, including the eye-catching 1923 Chanel suit and her range of little black dresses.

Iris Apfel

'People like me because I'm different.'

29 AUGUST 1921 –
UNITED STATES

Iris is famous for her eccentric style, combining her signature oversized-glasses with bold jewellery and varying textiles. Her outfits possess so much flair that in September 2005, The Metropolitan Museum of Art housed a collection of some of Iris' most original styles. As an expert in antique fabrics, Iris is an interior designer who has worked on numerous high-profile projects, including at the White House. Iris is also a celebrated jewellery designer and writer, and is the star of the 2014 documentary *Iris*. Her originality has made her one of the most enduring icons in design.

Mary Quant

'It is very important to take enormous risks.'

11 FEBRUARY 1934 –
UNITED KINGDOM

Mary is known for her revolutionary designs, particularly those she created in the 60s. Credited as creating the mini-skirt, not to mention the very first pair of hot pants, Mary reinvented women's hemlines. In the process, she paved the way for women to wear less conservative clothes and pushed the fashion industry into more creative territory.

Maggie Tabberer

'And remember, girls, whatever you do,
be good at it.'

11 DECEMBER 1936 –
AUSTRALIA

After a successful modelling and TV career, Maggie became the Fashion Editor of *The Australian Women's Weekly* in 1981. For 15 years she became a leader of the conversations surrounding fashion in Australia and became known as a style icon. Maggie has been recognised for her contribution to the Australian fashion industry through numerous awards, including the 1998 Order of Australia. In 1984 she became the first woman to receive the Sir Charles McGrath Marketing Award.

Vivienne Westwood

'Fashion is very important. It is life-enhancing and, like everything that gives pleasure, it is worth doing well.'

8 April 1941 –
United Kingdom

Vivienne is a rebel with many causes. Her unwillingness to follow convention led her to spearhead the punk rock movement in the 1970s. Known for combining leather with zippers, platform heels and a punk attitude, Vivienne has gone on from having one small store in 1971 to a global brand that is one of the most recognisable in the world, making everything from jewellery and swimsuits to bridal couture. Vivienne campaigns for fewer clothes to be produced in the fashion industry and to improve the quality of the clothes that are made so that they last longer to reduce the environmental devastation that results from garments ending up in landfill each year.

Guo Pei

'With the success of every show or every recognition, I'm motivated to do even better.'

12 March 1967 –
China

Guo started sewing when she was only two years old and found she loved making her own clothes. After graduating from design school in 1986, Guo used her extraordinary creativity to produce some of the most elaborately striking designs in modern fashion. Guo loves to tell stories through her clothes by weaving fairy tales and legends into her work. Pairing her ancestral Chinese heritage with modern innovation and style, Guo's show-stopping designs have appeared in film, the 2008 Beijing Olympics and the 2015 Met Gala where Rihanna wore one of Guo's dresses. Galleries around the world, from Paris to Melbourne, have showcased Guo's designs – allowing the public to access to her exquisite imagination.

Neeta Lulla

'To be honest, I prefer not to get a day off. I love working; I always carry my designing pad and pencil wherever I go.'

5 March 1971 –
India

Neeta is a costume designer, fashioning some of the most eye-catching pieces in Bollywood cinema. Having designed for over 300 films, Neeta also manages a successful business that creates both runway pieces and bridal couture lines. Neeta draws on the fashion of traditional Indian dress and plays with the exquisite intricacy and drama of these designs, while combining them with cutting-edge in-vogue styles.

Lan Yu

'I am glad to see the world moving away from telling women that they can't wear certain items of clothing because they look a certain way – all women are beautiful.'

21 January 1986 –
China

When she was only six, Lan's mother began teaching her Suzhou embroidery, a traditional form of Chinese silk embroidery known for its delicate needlework that renders beautiful artistic designs. Lan fell in love with design and in 2005, as a young design student, she launched her design workshop LANYU. Focusing on couture that combines traditional Chinese design elements with a feminine modern twist, often creating very whimsical looks on the catwalk, Lan's label also creates wedding dresses, accessories and ready-to-wear pieces. As one of the most iconic designers in China, Lan has won numerous awards, including Asia's Most Influential Designer at the Asian Fashion Awards in 2012.